This book TALKS!

Touch ANYTHING you see!
Here's what the buttons do:

LEVEL 1
Touch here
to PLAY an
activity!

LEVEL 2
Touch here to
start a MORE
CHALLENGING
activity!

Need a
hint?
Touch
here.

THIS
STOPS
EVERYTHING!

Ready to start the fun? Turn the page!

TEACHES ✓ Addition and subtraction with *more than* and *less than*

Omnidroid Add and Subtract

10 11 2 14 18 4 16 3 9

3

LAP 1

LAP 2

LAP 3

LAP 4

LAP 5

5 10 15 20 25 30

Time Trials

LAP 1

LAP 2

LAP 3

LAP 4

LAP 5

35　40　45　50　55　60

TEACHES
- ✔ Match numbers and written numerals
- ✔ Use position words

One   Two   Three   Four   Five

Six   Seven   Eight   Nine   Ten

Listen and Count

▲		●		■
100		10		0
200		20		1
300		30		2
400		40		3
500		50		4
600		60		5
700		70		6
800		80		7
900		90		8
				9

ESCAPE FROM NOMANISAN ISLAND

A. ● + ■ = 34

B. ● + ■ = 17

C. ● + ■ = 92

D. ● + ■ = 53

E. ● + ■ = 86

F. ● + ■ = 21

G. ● + ■ = 75

H. ● + ■ = 48

I. ▲ + ● + ■ = 235

J. ▲ + ● + ■ = 519

K. ▲ + ● + ■ = 182

L. ▲ + ● + ■ = 860

M. ▲ + ● + ■ = 451

N. ▲ + ● + ■ = 694

O. ▲ + ● + ■ = 323

P. ▲ + ● + ■ = 746

4921 | I 02 0324 65983 I 654 I 5456 4921 | I 02 0324 65983 I 654 I 5456 4921 | I 02 0324 65983 I 654 I 5456

9

TEACHES
✓ Identify symmetry
✓ Analyze data in bar graphs

Symmetry Simulator

12

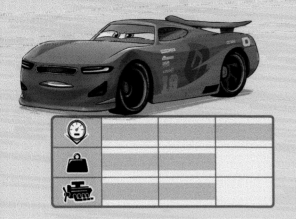

⏱			
⚖			
⚙			

⏱			
⚖			
⚙			

STATS Challenge

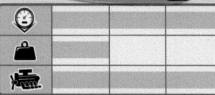

⏱			
⚖			
⚙			

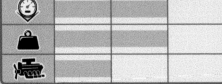

⏱			
⚖			
⚙			

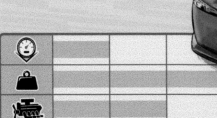

⏱			
⚖			
⚙			

10

50 100

Dory and Hank
TANK MATCH

16

TEACHES
- Skip count by 2s, 5s, and 10s
- Determine the number 10 more than

1   2   3   4   5

11   12   13   14   15

21   22   23   24   25

31   32   33   34   35

41   42   43   44   45

SKIP COUNT with Dash + Violet

6   7   8   9   10

16   17   18   19   20

26   27   28   29   30

36   37   38   39   40

46   47   48   49   50

OIL CAN
Addition

TEACHES
- ✓ Count sets of items
- ✓ Add doubles

2 4 6 8 10 12 14 16 18 20

Stingray Sets

23

Even

0

2

4

6

8

Odd

1

3

5

7

9

Some even
Some odd

25

TEACHES
- ✓ Practice ordinal numbers
- ✓ Listen to differentiate clues

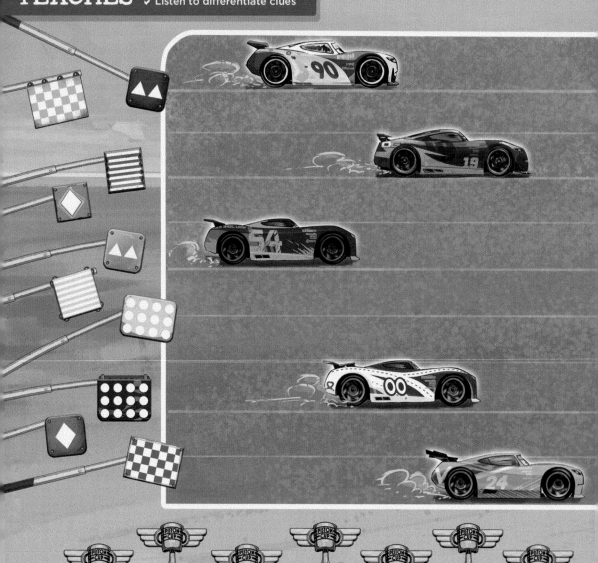

Who's in First?

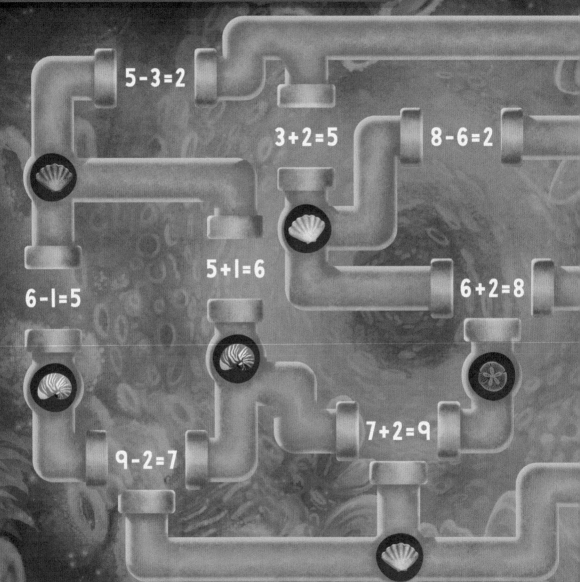

$$5-3=2$$

$$3+2=5$$

$$8-6=2$$

$$5+1=6$$

$$6+2=8$$

$$6-1=5$$

$$7+2=9$$

$$9-2=7$$

START

PIPE
problems

7 - 3 = 4

4 + 3 = 7

5 + 0 = 5

5 - 5 = 0

6 - 2 = 4

2 + 4 = 6

FINISH

My Rewards

Numbers, Counting, and Sets

Count forwards and backwards within 100

Skip count by 2s, 5s, and 10s

Determine even and odd numbers

Practice ordinal numbers

Use place value to create
two- and three-digit numbers

© 2018 Disney/Pixar

Geometry and Data

Identify 2D and 3D shapes

Determine symmetry

Interpret data in a graph

Listening Skills

Follow directions and use position words

Interpret descriptions to match data

Differentiate clues

Remember details

Spring into reading with **Ball On The Run** and more
in the LEARN TO READ VOLUME 1 six-book set!

Kate hit the ball.
She ran for the base.

Kate was so happy.
Just look at her face.

LEVEL 1
PRESCHOOL

LEVEL 2
PRE-KINDERGARTEN

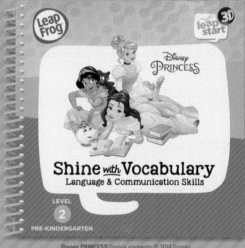

Leap Frog · LeapStart 3D

Disney MICKEY AND THE ROADSTER RACERS

Pit Crews to the Rescue
A LeapStart® Storybook

LEVEL 1
PRESCHOOL

Reading Comprehension
Vocabulary · Teamwork

Disney Junior

Leap Frog · LeapStart 3D

Disney PRINCESS

Shine with Vocabulary
Language & Communication Skills

LEVEL 2
PRE-KINDERGARTEN

Leap Frog · LeapStart 3D

123
Scout & Friends Math
with Problem Solving

LEVEL 1
PRESCHOOL

Leap Frog · LeapStart 3D

PAW PATROL

Around Town
with PAW PATROL
Jobs, Places, and Problem Solving

LEVEL 2
PRE-KINDERGARTEN

 2-5 years Teaches early fundamentals like ABCs, as well as shapes, colors & creativity.

3-6 years Introduces early key skills like phonics, writing, counting & critical thinking.